ed   ch of the

HOPSC
HISTO

The Song of Boudica

by Mick Gowar

Illustrated by Mark Beech

FRANKLIN WATTS
LONDON•SYDNEY

About this book

Some of the characters in this book are made up, but the story is based on real events in history. The Romans first invaded Britain in 55 BCE, led by Julius Caesar. At the time, Britain was made up of lots of different tribes. Boudica became Queen of the Iceni tribe (based in East Anglia) after the death of her husband, King Prasutagus, in CE 60. She formed an army from many different tribes to fight the Romans. At first, she had great success. The rebel army destroyed the Roman town of Colchester, burned down London and ransacked St Albans before the Romans finally defeated Boudica and the rebels.

First published in 2009 by
Franklin Watts
338 Euston Road
London
NW1 3BH

Franklin Watts Australia
Level 17/207 Kent Street
Sydney
NSW 2000

Text © Mick Gowar 2009
Illustrations © Mark Beech 2009

The right of Mick Gowar to be identified as the author
and Mark Beech as illustrator of this Work has been asserted
in accordance with the Copyright, Designs and Patents Act, 1988.

A CIP catalogue record for this book is available
from the British Library.

ISBN 978 0 7496 8576 8 (hbk)
ISBN 978 0 7496 8582 9 (pbk)

Series Editor: Melanie Palmer
Series Advisor: Dr Barrie Wade
Series Designer: Peter Scoulding

Printed in China

Franklin Watts is a division of
Hachette Children's Books,
an Hachette UK company
www.hachette.co.uk

My name is Bram the bard.

I travel around Britain

singing my song.

When I was a boy, our people, the Icenci, were ruled by King Prasutagus. Queen Boudica was his wife.

4

King Prasutagus told us:
"The Roman soldiers are our
friends. They will protect us
from our enemies."

When the King died, Queen
Boudica, became our ruler.
She didn't trust the Romans.

They stole the King's treasure
and made my people their slaves.

Boudica told us to get ready
for war. Our warriors sharpened
their swords and spears.

My father was her chariot driver –
the best and fastest in Britain!

Boudica was the best warrior of all.
She was taller and stronger than
any man.

She could throw a spear
further than
any man ...

and fight with a sword
better than any man.

One day she gave a great speech:

"The Romans are not our friends.

We can beat the Roman army!

We can send them back to Italy!"

Soon many warriors had joined
Boudica's army. They marched to
the town of Colchester, where
many Romans lived.

The Romans had built a great temple to their Emperor, Claudius. They thought he was a god.

The Romans couldn't stop Boudica's army. Our warriors smashed the statue of Claudius and burned the temple and the city to the ground!

Then our army marched to London. When the Roman soldiers saw our warriors coming, they ran away!

Our warriors burned London
to the ground, too.

And in every fight my father was in the first chariot. He drove the horse while Boudica threw her spears or fired her arrows.

My father said I could come with
him and watch the next battle.

"We'll smash the Roman army, son" he said. "We'll drive them back to Italy!"

I sat on top of the wagon and watched. Our warriors yelled their war cries. Our chariots charged.

25

But this time the Roman soldiers
did not run away. They fought back.

They threw their spears.

They stabbed with their swords.

Their horses charged.

The Romans won the battle. Most of our warriors died – including my father and Queen Boudica.

But one day I am sure our warriors
will beat the Roman army and
drive them back to Italy!

Puzzle 1

Put these pictures in the correct order.

Which event do you think is most important?

Now try writing the story in your own words!

Word Bank

Bard
Battle
Chariot
Roman
War
Warrior

What do these pictures tell you about

Boudica and the way of life at the time?

How are things different today?

You can use the word bank to help you.

Answers

Puzzle 1

The correct order is: 1c, 2a, 3e, 4f, 5d, 6b.

Puzzle 2

Life in Britain was very different in Boudica's time.

Think about tribes, armies, invasions and towns.

To find out more, try this book:

The Romans, (Starting History), Sally Hewitt, Franklin Watts, 2006